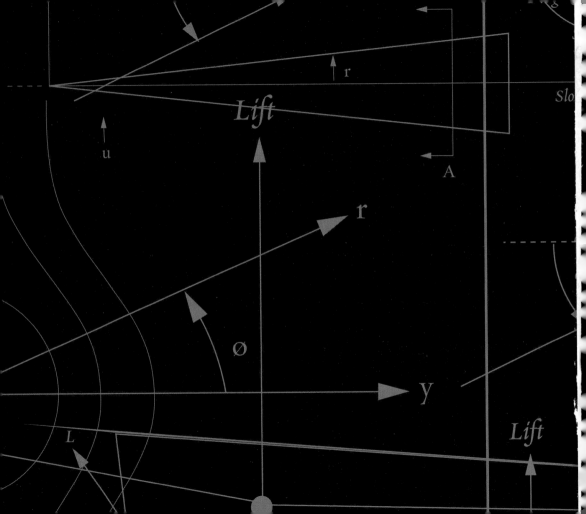

Paper Airplane: A Lesson for Flying Outside the Box

Michael McMillan

Published by:
SIMPLE TRUTHS
1952 McDowell Road, Suite 300
Naperville, IL 60563
800.900.3427
simpletruths.com

Written/designed by:
MICHAEL MCMILLAN
680 North Lake Shore Drive, Suite 2800
Chicago, IL 60611
michaelmcmillan.com

02 WOZ 13

Library of Congress Cataloging-in-Publication
Data is available.

Design/photography: Elizabeth Choi, Megan
Kearney, Michael McMillan, Charlie Westerman

Thanks to: Tom Doty, Alice McMillan,
Char Rapoport Nance, Lisa Sanderson,
Paul Turnbaugh, Will Wells, Pam Williams

Printed/bound in the United States of America.

Anne, thank you for providing your knowledge and understanding...
Mark, Paul and Sara, your diverse views are valued
and provide much insight.

This story has little to do with the science

In fact, the information about aerodynamic

It's more about vision, courage and

reality for his classmates, teacher...

or the Art of making paper airplanes.

t flying is somewhat limited.

a sixth grade boy's ability to change

and maybe even those who read this book.

SOUTHE

Mr. L. Uhr
Mrs. Hack

SCHOOL

Principal
- Grade 6

The intensity of the rush left me fighting to understand.

time stopped

. 9 . 8 . 7 . 6 . 5 . 4 . 3 . 2 . 1 .

It forced me

to keep that

precise moment

alive forever—

creating

an experience

that said:

"I was taken b

Today, people call it thinking "out-of-the-box" or "paradigm-shift" thinking—

seeing something in an entirely different way.

Taking action on ideas to achieve breakthrough results sounds good in theory. But experience teaches us the consequences of going against what is accepted— and believed to be correct. Even the best ideas can result in failure, often because of people's resistance to change. So why expend the energy? Why risk failure trying to change what's already "right"?

Throughout our lives, we are taught standard patterns of acceptable thinking. These patterns influence our laws, politics and religions. In short, they become our reality, our truth. So naturally, whenever they're challenged, and better results occur, the outcome can have a great impact. Ultimately, accepted practices give way to different forms of thinking, and another "right" way of doing things is born, causing us to readjust our thinking and adapt to a new reality.

"Open your books so we can review our section on aerodynamics. Once we're finished, we'll go outside and do an experiment that involves a contest."

"Over the past week, we've studied many of man's attempts to fly. We've learned how two self-taught brothers made history on December 17, 1903, by being the first to sustain controlled, powered flight. While the flight lasted only 12 seconds, the plane they built managed to fly 120 feet."

"What made the Wright brothers believe they could successfully build a machine that could fly when everyone else before them had failed, and often died trying?"

"Yes, Nancy?"

"Orville Wright studied everything he could about flying. He looked at how birds flew. He figured out that they moved the tips of their wings to keep their balance and steer. Oh, yeah. He also flew kites."

"Okay, good, Nancy. Orville realized that birds maintained lateral control by using the tips of their wings—something others had overlooked. And you're right, he used kites and gliders to test some of his thinking."

"But, remember, the Wright Brothers found that the accepted information on flying was wrong, so they had to establish their own. Their breakthrough thinking launched a new field of science and changed the way the world looked at flying."

"Before we start our
experiment, consider what we've learned
about velocity, weight and surface forces—drag, lift and thrust.
Think about wing shapes and how they are engineered to cut through the air.
Remember, the more streamlined the shape, the less resistance. And less resistance results
in faster planes that can travel farther."

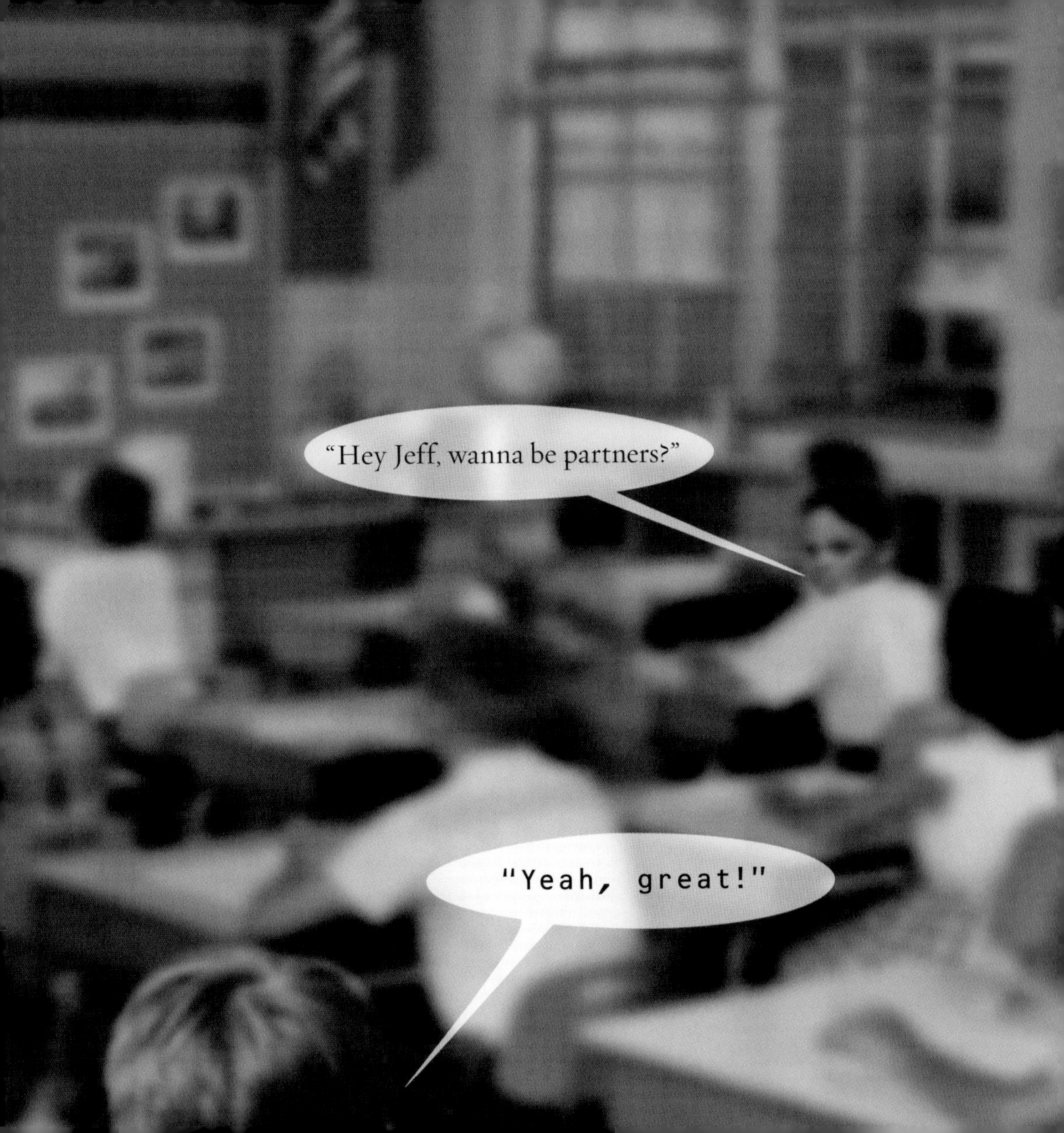
"Hey Jeff, wanna be partners?"
"Yeah, great!"

```
J E F F E W A S A E G O O D O C F R I E N D
W D F H E I L I K E D W F H T O M F H G C F
J A D E A A H D O T A J D O A A J D O A H D
F P C R E A T I V E O F S T A L K S E I A S
R R T O E H A Q Y E E R Q Y T O R H I M L Q
C L V E A I Y V B A A L V E B A B V E M I V
P A R A D I G M E M I A U I E E W I D U S R
C D E C O M I B C U P W I N S H I F T F H E
O T O P U N E S A U U E S M N I E S T F U S
U B R A L T U E U C F L I G H T O E L I N E
R P M P E Q J O S E A P R Z S E U N Z N W R
A U S E K U U H E A L W A Y S H I E T Y S S
G E S E E M E D I H B E Y E H T A W I S H G
E L V U J J T V U F I N D M E A N I N G J V
S D P O K L O P E U G I O N T H I N G S T P
O N L M K H I L P K R I L P K Q H D P Y A L
T F O E O F T A E E F T H I F F D A Y F F A
S S I W C S S I H C C S I N Z C I I N L C I
C H A N G E T T Q R R O E Q R R D E Q R A E
A C T I O N O E A O P E O P L E N E A O O N
E E S A I R P L A N E E S F O U T H W D N S
```

Jeff was always coming up with things to make people laugh. Some people might say he was the class clown, but Tom didn't think of him that way.

He was really smart, but unlike Tom, he didn't do so well in school. Perhaps he could have done well…

Actually, it's hard to tell.

He was a dreamer. It seemed like he always had something else on his mind—something that only he understood. So he rarely discussed the topic at hand, unless it was open for a new point of view.

He just seemed bored and restless like school held him back from discovering life's great secrets.

Jeff was an unusual kid. Better yet, he was unique.

At any given time, he could be staring out the window in deep thought, sharing a theory he had been pondering, making the class laugh, or challenging the relevance of the daily assignment.

Depending on whom you asked, Jeff was viewed as a smart kid who didn't apply himself, a young man who marched to a different beat, or in many cases, a kid who caused trouble by not following directions—challenging the status quo.

Good or bad, he was usually on some sort of mission. He didn't quit when he put his mind to something.

Jeff liked making things happen—he also liked winning.

That's the other reason Tom wanted him as his partner!

"Come up front and get a piece of construction paper."

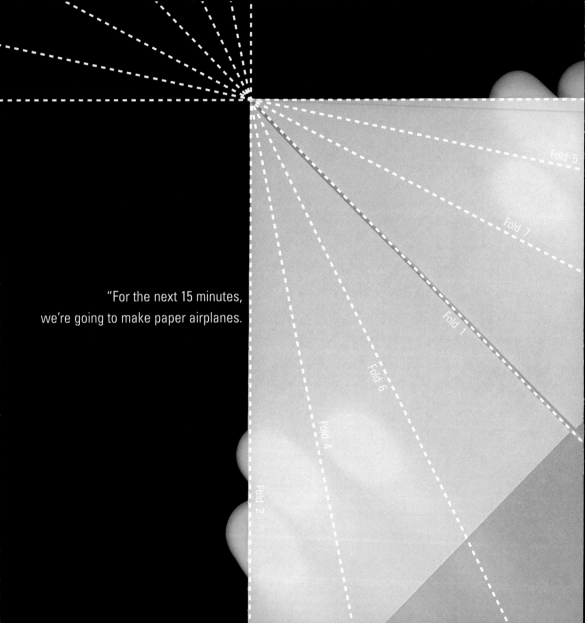

"For the next 15 minutes,
we're going to make paper airplanes.

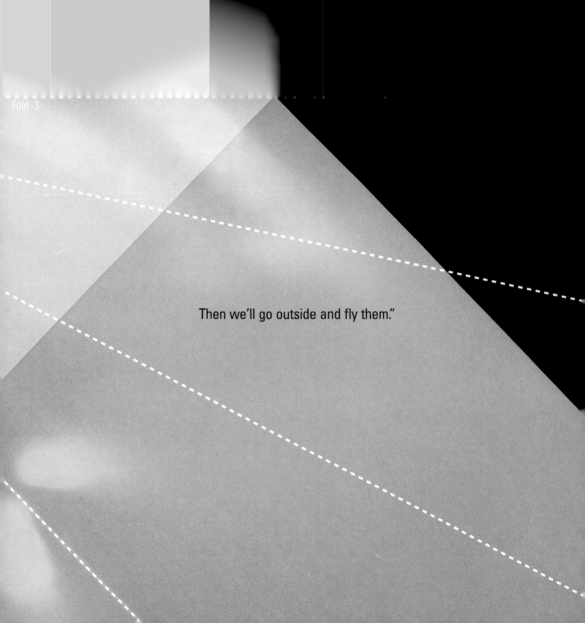

Then we'll go outside and fly them."

"The Dart"

"The Dragon"

"The Bomber"

"The High Flyer"

"The Super Fighter"

"The Creeper"

"The Kite"

"The Magellan"

"Any questions?

Yes, Sara?"

"Can we color our planes?"

"Good question. Do you have enough time?

Will coloring make them go farther?"

"Jeff, what kind of plane are you gonna make?"

"Don't know yet," Jeff said in a state of deep thought.

"Well, I think I'm gonna do a regular kind of fold, except this time,

"We're gonna win. I can feel it." Tom replied, trying to be a positive partner, before saying,

I'm gonna make the sharpest point possible to cut through the air."

Ten minutes passed

Tom was all finished with his plane and had his popsicle stick marker ready to go.

Jeff was still thinking.

"Everyone line up with your partner. We're going to put your planes to the test."

All of the planes looked pretty much the same.

Some were nicer than others.

One looked like a nosedive waiting to happen.

Another looked like it could fly for a mile if the wind was right.

But with Jeff's unfolded sheet of paper in hand, they were destined for last place.

"Jeff, anything's better than nothing at all."

anyt

hing

Jeff still hadn't made a single crease in his paper.

Tom was really beginning to question his choice of partners.

To buy some time, he asked Mrs. Hackett if they could go last.

"Yes, she said it was okay, Jeff. We're up last."

The experiment was interesting with many unexpected twists.

Teams	Distance
Team 1	✖ ✖
Team 2	
Team 3	✖
Team 4	Some planes barely flew five feet. ✖
Team 5	✖ ✖
Team 6	✖
Team 7	✖
Team 8	✖
Team 9	
Team 10	

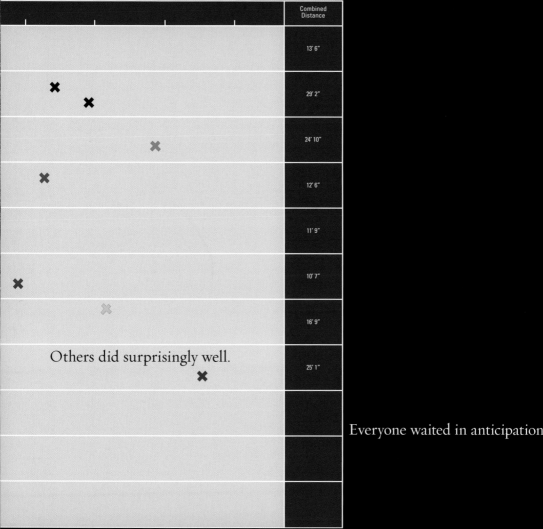

	Combined Distance
	13' 6"
	29' 2"
	24' 10"
	12' 6"
	11' 9"
	10' 7"
	16' 9"
Others did surprisingly well.	25' 1"

Everyone waited in anticipation

But one thing was certain: The line was thinning down...

Jeff was still holding a flat piece of construction paper.

"Tom and Jeff, you're next."

"Just go, don't worry about me."

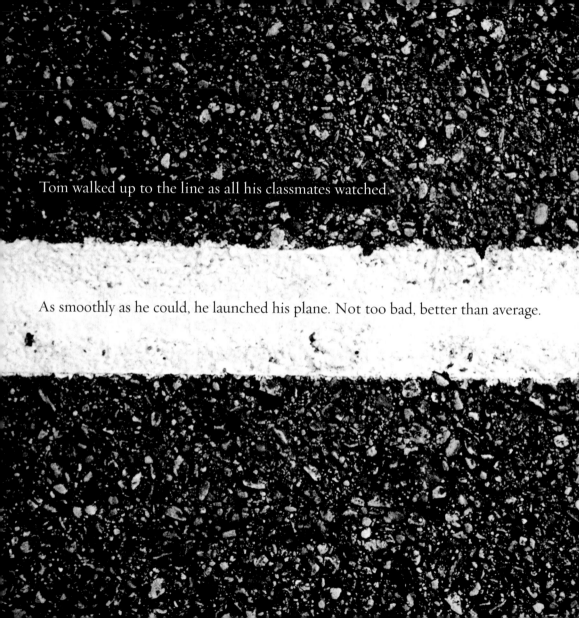

Tom walked up to the line as all his classmates watched.

As smoothly as he could, he launched his plane. Not too bad, better than average.

If Jeff could only duplicate his distance, they'd be serious contenders.

Jeff approached the line with his craft well hidden behind his back.

Then he exposed his masterpiece—a flat, unviolated sheet of paper.

With great confidence...

He wadded up the paper into a ball

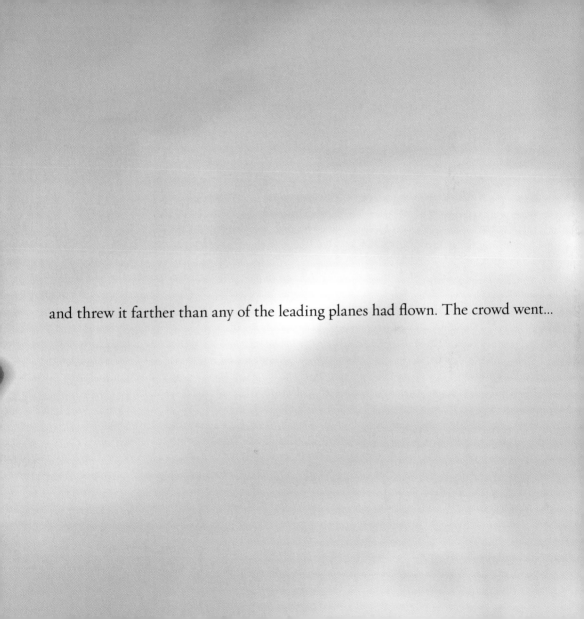

and threw it farther than any of the leading planes had flown. The crowd went...

Nobody was certain how to feel or what to say, not even Mrs. Hackett.

Everyone was taken by the moment.

Jeff explained that to his way of thinking, by crumpling the paper into a ball, he could throw his plane with more force—kind of like a baseball. And because there was no wing interference—it was able to travel the greatest distance.

Jeff interpreted a problem in a new way and had the courage to act on his vision.

Mrs. Hackett's sixth-grade class would never be the same.

Looking back in front of me

While Jeff's paper airplane approach was new to his class, the concept of "breakthrough" ideas and "paradigm shifts"... or, whatever you choose to call it has been around since the beginning of time. Solving problems is at the foundation of our survival. There have always been people who thought differently, or did something in a new way. They're the ones responsible for nearly every subject taught today. Good or bad, the vision and determination of creative people have and will continue to impact our lives.

In a way, learning and finding breakthrough concepts can be viewed as a journey of sorts. However, on this Journey, there's usually too little time to determine your own destination, much less the way you'll travel. Instead, you've handed a Map with detailed instructions telling you where to go and how to get there. Maps simply explain the territory you've yet to explore. They're based on information and understanding gained by earlier travelers. While maps can be helpful, they can also be detrimental to creative thinking. If you follow them too closely, you can miss information not seen or understood by the map's creator.

Because most people prefer safe, predictable results, "proven" maps are usually handed out and followed closely. They are considered objective, therefore making them easier to teach and establish a standard against which to measure. Without realizing it, you're thinking inside-the-box. Jeff however, took a different path. He traveled through uncharted territory and found a new solution to a problem. And, in doing so, he risked experiencing undesirable results, viewed by most people as failure.

the potential of Jeff's plane always existed—it's just that nobody in the class had ~~taken the time~~ their eyes off the map they'd been handed. If they did, they either missed it or feared getting lost. They were just doing what they were taught—following the proven map, then showing how well they understood it by folding and flying their planes accordingly.

I've always found it interesting that throughout history nearly all people now recognized as brilliant mostly ignored the maps they were given. And contrary to what's typically explained, it's not because they mastered the proven maps first and then moved on. It's because they didn't understand or accept them, so they created their own.

The map Jeff's teacher provided was based on solid aviation information developed by intelligent people dedicated to finding new answers. It was a good map. However, it dealt more with engine-powered airplanes—not paper ones. Sometimes a good map is applied to the wrong territory. When this happens, you can get more lost than if you had no map at all. I think most maps are originally created with solid intentions—whether it's getting from (A) (B) or whatever. It's just that over time unrelated information and agendas are slowly added to them. People spend (too much) time and energy focusing on the wrong issues, and once again, thinking inside-the-box appears.

If people are respectfully allowed to think, grow and contribute with their individual abilities, we will learn much faster about the unseen truths that surround us each day. By letting people create their own maps, we will build momentum for discovery and achieve more profound insight and understanding.

Perhaps this story will serve as an idea map — challenged by every one who reads it. Hopefully, it will be improved or replaced by some one more capable of seeing things I missed along the way, on my journey. I don't have all the answers... No one does. Maybe that's a good starting point when we think about important things like raising children, establishing educational programs, building businesses — leading fulfilling lives.

Since the beginning of time, creative thinking followed by action has separated the survivors from those unable or unwilling to see new possibilities and change. Creativity distinguishes the winners from the losers.

Michael McMillan has a well-deserved reputation for creative thinking and delivering innovative results. Early in his career, Michael founded a graphic design firm that soon attracted a client roster that read like the *Who's Who* of Business. *Fortune* 500 corporations, small entrepreneurial businesses, sports and music legends, non-profit organizations and institutions have sought Michael's creative input and guidance to deliver effective visual communication solutions with award-winning results. His work has been recognized by major design, marketing, advertising and communication organizations around the world.

Michael's creative direction on Michael Jordan's *New York Times* best-selling pictorial autobiography, *Rare Air*, established a new niche in retail publishing. He followed this success with several more award-winning coffee-table books including *Mario Andretti, The NBA at 50* and John Deere's *Genuine Value*.

After 20 consecutive years of growth, Michael sold his firm to pursue new challenges and opportunities. He collaborated with Mac Anderson, founder of Successories and Simple Truths, to create *The Race*, a gift book based on a poem stressing the importance of never giving up. Struck by the book's impact, Michael wrote and directed a short film that has received accolades from a diverse international audience.

Michael also worked with Ken Blanchard and Barbara Glanz to produce *Johnny the Bagger: The Simple Truths of Service*, a book about the importance of customer service that comes from the heart. To date, the online video Michael created based on the book has been viewed by more than 10 million people.

Recently, Michael coauthored *The Power of Teamwork* with former Blue Angels pilot Scott Beare. This compelling book explores the essence of teamwork and reinforces key principles embraced by the Blue Angels.

Michael's breadth of knowledge and experience, combined with his story-telling ability, make him a much-sought-after public speaker. His message connects with audiences of all ages, leaving them both motivated and committed to embrace a future of endless possibilities.

To learn more visit: michaelmcmillan.com

THE POWER OF
TeamWork
Inspired by The Blue Angels

Scott Beare & Michael McMillan

212°
the extra degree

Sam Parker / Mac Anderson

DREAMS
ARE WHISPERS FROM THE SOUL

Finding Your Purpose and Passion in Life

by MARCIA WIEDER

You Can't
Send a Duck
to Eagle School

And Other Simple Truths of Leaders

Mac Anderson

The Dash
Making a Difference with Your Life

Linda Ellis & Mac Anderson

Great Quotes
FROM
Great Leaders

PEGGY ANDERSON

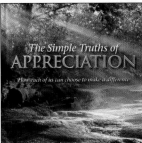
The Simple Truths of
APPRECIATION
How each of us can choose to make a difference

Barbara A. Glanz

TO A CHILD LOVE
IS SPELLED
T-I-M-E

what a child really needs from

MAC ANDERSON & LANCE WUBBELS

The STRANGEST
SECRET
HOW TO LIVE THE LIFE YOU DESIRE

EARL NIGHTINGALE

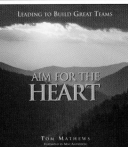
LEADING TO BUILD GREAT TEAMS

AIM FOR THE
HEART

TOM MATHEWS
FOREWORD BY Mac Anderson

The
Simple Truths
of Service

Inspired by Johnny the Bagger

By Ken Blanchard & Barbara Glanz

The Power of
ATTITUDE

MAC ANDERSON
FOUNDER
SUCCESSORIES

Paper Airplane
A Lesson for Flying
Outside the Box

Michael McMillan

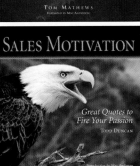
SALES MOTIVATION

Great Quotes to
Fire Your Passion
TODD DUNCAN

Introduction by Mac Anderson

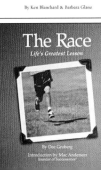
The Race
Life's Greatest Lesson

By Dee Groberg
Introduction by Mac Anderson
founder of Successories

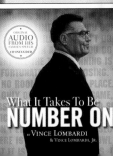
ORIGINAL
AUDIO
FROM HIS
FAMOUS SPEECH
CD INCLUDED

What It Takes To Be
NUMBER ONE

BY VINCE LOMBARDI
& VINCE LOMBARDI, JR.

GREAT GIFT BOOKS...

FOR YOUR EMPLOYEES AND CUSTOMERS

If you have enjoyed this book and wish to order additional copies,

or if you would like to learn more about our

full line of inspirational gift books, please visit us at

simpletruths.com

or call us toll free at

800.900.3427

Please note that our books are not sold through bookstores or other retail outlets.

They can be purchased direct from Simple Truths or a Simple Truths distributor.

We look forward to serving you.

Have you ever thoughT tHere'd bE a day when peoplE thiNk a Different way?
And on that day, what would you say, if you still thought the other way?

—*Paul McMillan* *

* *As I was finishing Paper Airplane, by accident I ran across this thought my son Paul had written down on a napkin in the 8th grade. In the end, it seems profoundly fitting.*

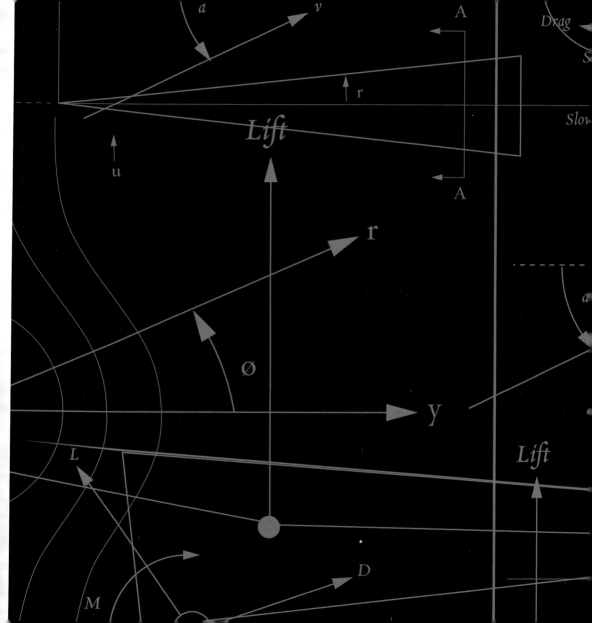